Bad Luck

by

C. L. Tompsett

Illustrated by Kevin Hopgood

First published in 2008 in Great Britain by
Barrington Stoke Ltd
18 Walker St, Edinburgh, EH3 7LP

www.barringtonstoke.co.uk

Title ISBN: 978-1-84299-626-3
Pack ISBN: 978-1-84299-623-2

Printed in Poland by Pozkal

We ask the author ...

What makes you feel sick?

When I go on holiday to France, my husband eats a little shellfish, called an oyster. He eats it when it is still alive. It makes me feel sick just to watch him. I tried to eat an oyster once and I could feel the live slimy thing sliding down my throat.

Ben was going home from school. He was looking down at the stone slabs of the path as he went.

He was trying not to step on the cracks between the slabs because that was bad luck.

Someone had told him this when he was little and he had not grown out of the habit.

He got home from school just after three.

He couldn't wait to take off his school things.

He ran up the stairs to his room, two at a time, as he always did. It was bad luck to walk on every step.

He came down the stairs, two at a time as well, but not on the same steps.

You see it was bad luck to walk on the same steps going up *and* down.

Ben went into the kitchen.

His mum wasn't cooking today.

"It's your dad's birthday," she said. "So we're going out for a meal."

"Great," said Ben. "Where are we going?"

He crossed his fingers for luck.

"We're going out for a pizza," Mum said.

"Yes!" Ben yelled.

Just what he liked. Crossing his fingers had worked.

At six o'clock, Ben's dad came home and they drove to 'The Pizza Place'.

Ben asked for a big pizza with extra cheese topping. He ate it all.

He was very full but he still ate a large ice cream.

Then at half past seven, they all went home.

By now Ben wasn't feeling very well.

He couldn't run up the stairs. He went very slowly and he had to use all the steps.

He knew it was bad luck.

He fell back on his bed.

His head was spinning and he had a bad pain in his guts.

He felt sick.

He went to the bathroom, lifted up the lid of the loo and sat down.

When he got up, he put the lid back down again.

That way, the THING that lived in the loo couldn't get out.

The THING in the loo had been there ever since he was little.

That night Ben had the runs and was very sick. He had to go to the loo again and again.

Each time he put the lid down.

But the last time he went, he forgot.

Ben sat on his bed. He was feeling very hot. The room was going round and round.

He lay down and shut his eyes.
Suddenly he heard an odd sound.

He heard a *flop*.

He heard a *slop*.

He heard a *slap*.

Ben looked over at the open door.

A big, brown THING was sliding along the floor.

It had yellow teeth. It had slime on its body. It was coming to get him!

He tried to get out of bed, but he was too weak.

Ben pulled the sheets over his head, but the THING pulled them off again.

It grabbed Ben and dragged him off to the loo.

Ben felt himself going under the water.
He was being pulled down into the loo.

It was dark down there.

He was very afraid.

He tried to get away, but the THING
held onto him.

Down and down they went.

Ben kicked the THING hard.

The THING let go.

At last he was free!

He swam back up, then he saw light.

He did not feel safe until he was back in bed, had put down the lid of the loo and shut his bedroom door.

Ben's door opened.

His mum came in.

"Are you awake?" she asked. "How are you feeling?"

Ben's mum was standing beside his bed with a torch.

"Have you had a bad dream?" she asked.

"You're shaking all over. And you're all wet."

"A big brown THING has just pulled me down the loo!" Ben told her.

Ben's mum put her hand on his head.

She felt his wet hair.

"You're not well," she said. "You're all hot. I think you must have a fever."

"You should not have eaten so much. You've had a bad dream. It's all these silly ideas you have. You are far too old for that now. There is no such thing as *bad luck*. And there is no THING in the loo!"

Ben crossed his fingers.